Good Morning, Snoopy!

Selected Cartoons from
KISS HER, YOU BLOCKHEAD!
Volume 3

Charles M. Schulz

CORONET BOOKS
Hodder and Stoughton

PEANUTS® by Charles M. Schulz

Copyright © 1982 by United Feature Syndicate Inc.

First published in the United States by
Ballantine Books in 1985

Coronet edition 1987

This book comprises a portion of KISS HER, YOU
BLOCKHEAD! and is reprinted by arrangement
with Holt, Rinehart and Winston

British Library C.I.P.

Schulz, Charles M.
  [Kiss her you blockhead!] Good morning,
  Snoopy!: selected cartoons from Kiss
  her you blockhead! Volume 3.
  I. [Kiss her you blockhead!]   II. Title
  741.5'973   PN6728.P4

  ISBN 0 340 40855 3

Printed and bound in Great Britain for
Hodder and Stoughton Paperbacks, a
division of Hodder and Stoughton Ltd.,
Mill Road, Dunton Green, Sevenoaks,
Kent (Editorial Office: 47 Bedford
Square, London, WC1B 3DP) by
Cox & Wyman Ltd., Reading.

Good Morning, Morning, SNOOPY!

THEY TOOK AWAY YOUR BASEBALL FIELD, CHARLES, AND YOU'RE NOT DOING ANYTHING ABOUT IT?

IS THIS HOW YOU'RE FIGHTING BACK... BY BOUNCING THAT STUPID GOLF BALL AGAINST THOSE STUPID STEPS?

WHAT DO YOU EXPECT ME TO DO?!

DON'T SCREAM, CHARLES.. IT'S EMBARRASSING...

I FIND IT DIFFICULT TO BELIEVE THAT THEY'VE TAKEN AWAY YOUR BALL FIELD, CHARLES, AND YOU'RE NOT FIGHTING BACK...

I FIND IT DIFFICULT TO BELIEVE THAT SOMEONE I AM VERY FOND OF COULD BE ACTING THIS WAY...

YOU'RE FOND OF **ME**?!

KISS HER, YOU BLOCKHEAD!

I THINK I JUST MADE A TOTAL FOOL OF MYSELF, SIR..I TOLD CHUCK I LIKED HIM, AND I KISSED HIM ON THE CHEEK!

IT WAS HIS OWN FAULT, SIR! THEY'VE TAKEN HIS BASEBALL FIELD FROM HIM, AND HE HASN'T DONE ANYTHING ABOUT IT!

HE'S NOT FIGHTING BACK! ALL HE'S DOING IS BOUNCING A GOLF BALL AGAINST THE STEPS!

HE MADE ME SO MAD, I TOLD HIM I LIKED HIM!

I THINK I FRIGHTENED POOR CHUCK...MAYBE IT'S A MISTAKE TO TALK SO OPENLY ABOUT LOVE...

NO, MARCIE, NO! YOU WERE JUST BEING HONEST!

REALLY, SIR? I DIDN'T THINK YOU KNEW ANYTHING ABOUT LOVE

MARCIE!

I DID IT AGAIN..

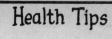

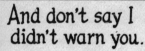

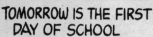

MY PEN IS LEAKING..I CAN'T OPEN MY BINDER..

BOTH PENCILS ARE BROKEN AND MY ERASER JUST BOUNCED UNDER SOMEONE'S DESK!

BE WITH YOU IN A MOMENT, MA'AM...

WE ARE EXPERIENCING TECHNICAL DIFFICULTIES!

I WON'T SAY THAT WOODSTOCK IS PREJUDICED

BUT SOMETIMES HIS OPINIONS ARE A LITTLE BIT SLANTED...

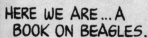

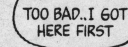

Travel Tips...
"Arriving Home"

When putting away your luggage after arriving home, always close the zippers so bugs can't crawl in.

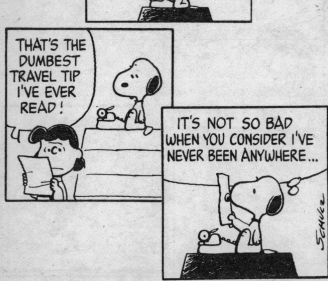

THAT'S THE DUMBEST TRAVEL TIP I'VE EVER READ!

IT'S NOT SO BAD WHEN YOU CONSIDER I'VE NEVER BEEN ANYWHERE...

HERE'S THE WORLD WAR I FLYING ACE HANGING AROUND THE BARRACKS...

HE IS RESTLESS.. THERE IS NOTHING TO DO EXCEPT PLAY CARDS...

OKAY, MEN, THE GAME IS "PIG"! IF YOU GET TWO OF A KIND, YOU PUT YOUR FINGER AGAINST YOUR NOSE LIKE THIS... GOT IT?

ACTUALLY, FLYING ACES VERY SELDOM PLAYED "PIG"

THE RED BARON HAS BEEN SIGHTED NEAR DOUAI...OUR MISSION IS TO BRING HIM DOWN...

SUDDENLY, ANTIAIRCRAFT FIRE BURSTS AROUND US!

IT DOES?

ONLY THE SUPERB SKILL OF THE FLYING ACE KEEPS THEM UNTOUCHED

HE WAS ALWAYS THE QUIET ONE IN THE FAMILY...

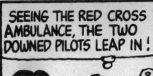

HEY, CHUCK.. I JUST SAW SNOOPY'S BROTHER GOING PAST OUR HOUSE.. I THOUGHT HE WAS LIVING WITH YOU...

I GUESS IT DIDN'T WORK OUT...REMEMBER WHAT MY AUNT MARIAN USED TO SAY?

"YOU CAN CHOOSE YOUR FRIENDS, BUT YOU CAN'T CHOOSE YOUR RELATIVES"

IT'S TOO BAD..WITH MY INFLUENCE, I COULD HAVE GOT HIM A GOOD JOB IN THE INFANTRY...

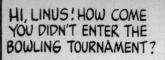

HEY, CHUCK, I SEE WE'RE BOWLING ON THE SAME LANES..AND LOOK AT THESE HANDICAPS...

MY AVERAGE IS 120 SO I GET 72 PINS..YOUR MISERABLE 85 AVERAGE GETS YOU 103 PINS... YOU'LL NEED 'EM, CHUCK..

WHAT'S THIS?! HERE'S SOMEBODY WITH A "ONE" AVERAGE! HE GETS 179 PINS! WHO WOULD TAKE A HANDICAP LIKE THAT?!!

JOE SANDBAGGER!

AVERAGE! HOW ... ANYBODY HAVE A "ONE" AVERAGE?

HERE'S JOE SANDBAGGER ROLLING THE FIRST BALL OF THE TOURNAMENT...

BEAR DOWN, JOE..YOU'RE GONNA DROP YOUR "ONE" AVERAGE!

THIS IS THE TENTH FRAME, SIR..YOU NEED A STRIKE...

ANOTHER SPLIT! RATS! THIS IS THE WORST GAME I'VE EVER BOWLED!!

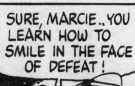

DO YOU THINK SPORTS BUILD CHARACTER, SIR?

SURE, MARCIE..YOU LEARN HOW TO SMILE IN THE FACE OF DEFEAT!

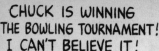

THERE I WAS, SITTING IN THE PUMPKIN PATCH...ALL OF A SUDDEN I HEARD A LOUD CRASHING NOISE! IT WAS THE "GREAT PUMPKIN"!

IT WAS A BOWLING BALL.. I GOT SO NERVOUS IN THE TENTH FRAME I THREW THE BALL OUT THE FRONT DOOR...

I'D NEVER SEEN THE "GREAT PUMPKIN" BEFORE... SUDDENLY, THERE HE WAS, FLYING RIGHT BY ME!

IT WAS A BOWLING BALL

I SHOULD HAVE WON THE TOURNAMENT, BUT I DIDN'T GET ANY BREAKS

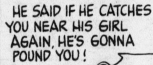

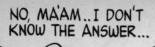

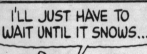

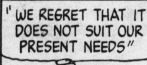

SO HERE I AM, ABOUT TO GO RIDING AGAIN ON THE BACK OF MY MOTHER'S BICYCLE...

TO QUOTE FROM THE BOOK OF "RUTH"...

"FOR WHITHER THOU GOEST, I WILL GO"

LIKE A BULLET!

"You love hockey more than you love me!" she complained.

"You love those hockey gloves, and shinguards, and skates and elbow pads more than you love me!"

"That's not true!" he said.

"I love you much more than I love my elbow pads."

I'M PRACTICING DRAWING CHRISTMAS WREATHS

THEY LOOK MORE LIKE DOUGHNUTS TO ME

DUNK A CHRISTMAS WREATH IN A CUP OF COFFEE, AND YOU'RE IN TROUBLE!

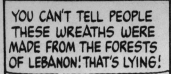

YOU CAN'T TELL PEOPLE THESE WREATHS WERE MADE FROM THE FORESTS OF LEBANON! THAT'S LYING!

GOOD MORNING.. WOULD YOU LIKE TO BUY A CHRISTMAS WREATH MADE FROM SOME JUNKY OL' BRANCHES MY BROTHER FOUND IN A CHRISTMAS TREE LOT?

YOU WOULDN'T, WOULD YOU? AND I CAN'T SAY I BLAME YOU!

SEE? YOUR WAY DOESN'T WORK, EITHER!

THIS IS A GREAT BUSINESS WE HAVE GOING HERE, BIG BROTHER...

YOU MAKE THE WREATHS, AND YOUR DOG AND I GO OUT AND SELL 'EM!

WE'LL SELL CHRISTMAS WREATHS TO EVERY HOME IN THE NEIGHBORHOOD

UNLESS MY NOSE FALLS OFF!

DO YOU THINK IT'S POSSIBLE THAT I'M YOUR FAVORITE PERSON IN THE WHOLE WIDE WORLD?

HAHAHAHA

SUDDENLY I'M A STAND-UP COMIC